# Garfield:
# that's life!

## JIM DAVIS

**Ballantine Books • New York**

A Ballantine Book
Published by The Ballantine Publishing Group

Copyright © 1998 by PAWS, Incorporated.

All rights reserved under International and Pan-American Copyright
Conventions. Published in the United States by The Ballantine Publishing
Group, a division of Random House, Inc., New York, and simultaneously in
Canada by Random House of Canada Limited, Toronto.

http://www.randomhouse.com

Library of Congress Catalog Card Number: 97-97176

ISBN: 0-345-42263-5

Manufactured in the United States of America

First Edition: April 1998

10  9  8  7  6  5  4  3  2

JIM DAVIS

9-17

SLAM!

VETERINARY CLINIC

SOMEHOW, THEY ALWAYS KNOW.

SPRING IS HERE

THE WARM SPRING SUN IS COAXING TREES TO BUD AND FLOWERS TO BLOOM. FLEDGLING SONGBIRDS ARE TESTING THEIR LILTING VOICES. SOFT SPRING ZEPHYRS ARE WAFTING THE SWEET SCENT OF LILACS. SPRING IS HERE

BIG, FAT HAIRY DEAL

© 1979 United Feature Syndicate, Inc.

4-3

JIM DAVIS

I JUST WANT YOU PEOPLE TO KNOW HOW MUCH WE CATS APPRECIATE YOU. WITHOUT YOU, WHO WOULD FEED US? WHO WOULD LOVE US?

4-28

AND MOST IMPORTANT OF ALL...

WHO WOULD CHANGE OUR KITTY LITTER?

JIM DAVIS

© 1979 United Feature Syndicate, Inc.

THAT'S A NASTY COLD YOU HAVE THERE, GARFIELD

SNIFF

© 1979 United Feature Syndicate, Inc.

WE'LL TAKE YOU TO THE VET AND GET YOU FIXED RIGHT UP

JIM DAVIS

NEVER SAY "FIXED" TO AN ANIMAL PERSON

11-24

WELL, GARFIELD, THAT'S THE LAST TIME THE HAMILTONS EVER ASK US OVER

© 1979 United Feature Syndicate, Inc.

JIM DAVIS

I HOPE YOU LEARNED A LESSON FROM THIS EVENING

I SURE DID

NEVER SHARPEN YOUR CLAWS ON A WATER BED

12-1

SNIFF

© 1980 United Feature Syndicate, Inc.  1-18

ARRRGH!!!

COLDS CAN BE FRUSTRATING CAN'T THEY, OL' BUDDY?

JIM DAVIS

YOUR COUGH SOUNDS BETTER, GARFIELD

HACK HACK

© 1980 United Feature Syndicate, Inc.

IT SHOULD

1-19

I'VE BEEN PRACTICING ALL NIGHT

JIM DAVIS

THE LIGHT BULB'S BURNED OUT

4-1 JIM DAVIS

DON'T WORRY ABOUT ME. I'LL JUST SIT HERE IN THE DARK GOING BLIND

I'LL FIX IT

HE'S SUCH A GOOD BOY

© 1981 United Feature Syndicate, Inc.

WHAT A NICE CHRISTMAS. I GOT AN EYE FOR MY TEDDY BEAR, SAND FOR MY SANDBOX, AND A NEW BLANKET

12-26 JIM DAVIS

THIS IS WHAT HAPPINESS IS ALL ABOUT...

© 1981 United Feature Syndicate, Inc.

SECURITY

AND NOW THE CONTINUING SAGA OF JON'S DIARY

Monday: "Dear Diary, The dawn of a new week. The possibilities are limitless"

Tuesday: "Dear Diary, Today I got my lips stuck in the blender"

JIM DAVIS 11-26

WHY WAS I CREATED, GARFIELD?

WHAT IS MY PURPOSE IN LIFE?

SPLOT!

TO GIVE OTHERS HOPE?

JIM DAVIS 11-27

JON IS DEEP IN THOUGHT

I WONDER HOW THEY GET THOSE PEANUTS INSIDE THE SHELLS?

RELATIVELY SPEAKING

© 1991 United Feature Syndicate, Inc.

JIM DAVIS 12-7

JIM DAVIS 12-11

KISS

GARFIELD, SANTA BRINGS TOYS TO THE LITTLE BOYS AND GIRLS WHO'VE BEEN GOOD ALL **YEAR**, NOT JUST THE LAST TWO WEEKS

© 1991 United Feature Syndicate, Inc.

THAT'S EXTORTION!

I TELL IT LIKE IT IS, BABY CAKES